Alzheimer's:
An Engineer's View

Fred Walker & Chris Pomfrett

Published in 2013 by:

Stellar Books Publishing LLP
Dunham Gatehouse
Charcoal Road
Bowdon
Cheshire
WA14 4RY

www.stellarbooks.co.uk

ISBN: 978-0-9565089-6-6

Dedication

This manuscript is dedicated to the memory
of Fred's wife, Joan.

Disclaimer

This work presents the personal opinions of Fred Walker and Chris Pomfrett, and not the opinions of their employers or sponsors.

Acknowledgements

Dr Eric Karran, Director of Research,
Alzheimer's Research UK.

Marek Holowenko, Chartered Physiotherapist.
07813769953 www.mhcpt.co.uk

Madhouse Associates,
Integrated Marketing Communications
196 Deansgate, Manchester, UK. M3 3WF
0161 819 6600
www.madhouseassociates.com

Contents

Biographies 1

Forward 3

Introduction 9

The body viewed by an Engineer 15

Early Signs 21

Early Symptoms 23

Clinical Interest 29

Diagnosis & Management 31

Coping and the Future 65

Helpful contact numbers 81

Biographies

Fred Walker

Fred's background is in engineering. Fred left Stretford Grammar School at 16 to take up a 2 year apprenticeship with the General Post Office in telecommunications. At 18, he was called up for National Service with the RAF and served in Gibraltar servicing anti-submarine radar in Shackleton bombers, which Fred had to air test before handing back to the squadron. On completion of service Fred returned to the GPO and when the company split into BT and The Post Office he stayed in the postal sector. Fred moved from telecommunications to Electric, Light and Power then on to Heating and Ventilation with a short period in Mechanical Engineering. After some years Fred transferred back to telecommunications where he became Regional Telecommunications Manager for the North West of England. Fred is now retired and spends time supporting Alzheimer's Research UK.

Chris Pomfrett

Chris is a Clinical Scientist. He holds a BSc. (1st Class Honours) from Queen Mary College, London University, in Comparative Physiology with Zoology, and a Ph.D. in Neurophysiology from the Medical College of St. Bartholomew's Hospital, London University. He has worked at Keele University (Research Fellow 1987-1989), Manchester University (Senior Research Assistant 1990-94, non-clinical lecturer in Neurophysiology applied to Anaesthesia 1994-2010), and has been a visiting Professor for a few months at the University of California, Irvine. Chris has worked as a Technical Adviser for the Medical Technologies Evaluation Programme of the National Institute of Health and Care Excellence (NICE) since 2011. Chris has a specialist interest in medical devices used for monitoring anaesthesia and diagnosing degenerative diseases of the nervous system.

Foreword

Dr Karen Drabble MB ChB

For Fred and Joan

I have been a doctor for almost 30 years – 25 of them as a GP in the same practice. Over these 25 years I have been privileged to be allowed into people's lives at a time when they are at their most vulnerable.

To be allowed into Fred and Joan's life during Joan's last months was one of the greatest privileges of my career. Their story is one of true love and devotion – to other people, their family and to one another.

I remember repeatedly asking Fred to allow me to arrange some respite care for Joan so that he could just have some sleep but he steadfastly refused and nursed Joan with such love and devotion that I was in awe of him.

Dementia is a cruel illness which affects people in different ways. No two stories are alike and people 'cope' in different ways. There is no right or wrong way to react to gradually losing a loved one. Everyone should read this booklet. Not only is it "Joan's Story" but it is also "Fred's Story."

The tale of how an engineer, with an engineer's perspective on life, managed to explain to himself what was happening to his wife.

"Fred's Story" goes on as he supports Alzheimer's Research UK in the hope of one day finding a cure for dementia. Hopefully that day is soon and this booklet will have helped.

Baroness Professor Susan Greenfield CBE

When I tell people, if asked what I do, that I research into Alzheimer's disease, the responses are invariably the same: 'What are the chances of a cure?' or 'Can you hurry up please and get something out there!' or 'My father/mother/ husband/wife has/had it...'and often the sentence stops there. Invariably the speaker looks sad and resigned, – and I feel helpless. What can I say that's positive, or sympathetic without sounding disingenuous, repeating some polite reply that must have heard a hundred times?

All of us fear Alzheimer's Disease, so much so that often we daren't even say the word in case that in itself is somehow contagious. Unlike heart disease or cancer, which are still very serious illnesses, Alzheimer's brings with it the added, devastating prospect of someone you love becoming like a highly dependent small child, whilst the companion with whom you shared so much, is gradually being lost to you...

4

For people facing up to this terrible possibility, or even for those who are interested on a less personal level on what having Alzheimer's actually means, Fred Walker's story will touch your heart and help you realise that you are not alone in what you might be experiencing. As an engineer he gives a hard-headed and honest account of the story of his wife's dementia that is then interpreted scientifically by Chris Pomfrett. As such it will be an invaluable guide to anyone who not only wants to know the facts, but who also needs to know the human cost behind those facts.

This account is important for all of us. The more we can shake off our prejudices and talk about Alzheimer's, the more we can all help each other bear the life-changing experiences it brings. And on a more mercenary note, the more we can raise awareness in this way, the more funding can be raised for research, so that eventually all of us can look forward not just to a longer life, but one that we'll be able to live to the full.

Dr Robert Jenyo MB: BS, FRCGP

This book is extremely well written and has all the warmth, humanity and honest insight into how someone experiences Alzheimer's dementia.

I feel quite privileged to have known Joan. She was truly a warm, caring, giving, loving and remarkable lady. She was obviously a wonderful wife, mother and grandmother who encouraged her husband at every hands turn.

This book is an eye-opener and a "must read" for everyone who has been touched by Alzheimer's in one way or another. It would also be especially beneficial to healthcare professionals. Enabling them to have a better understanding into, not only the science behind Alzheimer's but also equipping them with the ability to appreciate the challenging situations encountered by many unpaid carers.

Ultimately this is an uplifting and inspirational book for anyone who's going through the difficult and often lonely ordeal of caring for a loved one who suffers from this devastating illness.

Thank you, Fred for writing this excellent book and for all the hard work you are still doing for the Alzheimer's Research UK.

Rebecca Wood, Chief Executive, Alzheimer's Research UK

By reading Fred's deeply moving story, anyone touched by Alzheimer's disease or any other form of dementia will know they are not alone. It chronicles the fears and frustrations, the love and laughter and the tears and trauma he and his late wife Joan experienced together.

Determined to care for Joan himself during her four year journey with Alzheimer's, Fred's devotion was unwavering. He stepped into her world of dementia and used his engineer's mind to develop solutions to cope with her increasing needs and changes in personality.

Since Joan died in 2010, Fred has been a determined supporter of our pioneering dementia research. We are proud to have his support and have acknowledged his outstanding efforts by making him a Champion of Alzheimer's Research UK.

We are hugely grateful to Fred, and his co-author and friend Chris, for kindly donating all the proceeds from An Engineer's View to the charity. We rely on public donations to fund our vital work and the money raised will bring us closer to finding ways to diagnose, prevent, treat and cure dementia – one of the biggest medical challenges of our lifetime.

Everyone who buys a copy of this story will give hope to the hundreds of thousands of people across the UK living with dementia today, as well as their families and future generations.

An Engineer's View is a wonderful lasting legacy to Joan. She would be proud to know that Fred's determination has led him on a new journey to help us achieve our vision of a world free from dementia.

Introduction

This book is primarily an account of Joan Walker's clinical progression, and how Fred dealt with it. Fred's account is in normal type. Chris has inserted sections to give more clinical and scientific detail, and Chris' input is in italic type.

The idea for this book arose over a coffee. Fred was keen to learn the physiology underlying Alzheimer's disease, and how changes in brain function can be detected in symptoms of the disease. This was for a presentation he was preparing on behalf of Alzheimer's Research UK. Chris was used to explaining how the brain and nervous system processes sensory information before and during anaesthesia and another degenerative nervous disease, variant Creutzfeld Jacob Disease. Fred and Chris considered that there was a need to communicate the relevant bits of this knowledge to carers and healthcare professionals dealing with Alzheimer's disease on a day-to day basis.

The engineer's view of the title has two perspectives. Fred cared for Joan from the perspective of a problem-solving engineer and husband. Fred also wanted to know more about dementia.

What is Dementia? Dementia is a global name for a group of progressive illnesses which share common features.

The World Health Organisation describe it as a syndrome due to disease of the brain, usually of a chronic or progressive nature including disturbance of the multiple higher cortical functions such as memory, thinking, orientation, comprehension, calculation, language and judgement. One factor we must remember is that dementia is a terminal condition and the prevalence of dementia increases with age. Some signs of dementia include loss of memory, decline in self-care, mood changes, personality changes and social withdrawal.

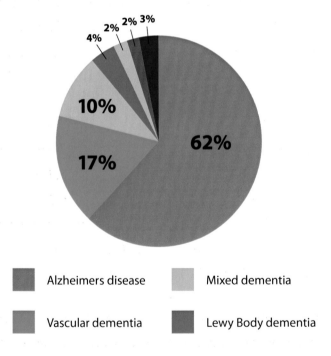

Figure 1: incidence of dementia – Dr Eric Karran Pers.com

There are many different forms of dementia, one of the most common being Alzheimer's disease in which the cerebral hemispheres shrink, nerve cells become damaged which causes failure in the transmission of signals from one nerve cell to another.

The cause of Alzheimer's disease is unknown, except for rare cases where it can be inherited. This is called familial Alzheimer's disease. For most, 'sporadic' cases of Alzheimer's disease, there is unlikely to be a single cause. Increasing age is also a major risk factor. The cure for Alzheimer's Disease is unknown. There are no medicines currently available that can deflect the course of, or prevent, Alzheimer's disease. Several therapies are available that offer modest symptomatic relief for short periods of time, but these do not affect the course of the disease. Some people have genetic types that increase the risk of developing Alzheimer's Disease. The genetic locus ApoE4 is a strong risk factor for Alzheimer's Disease and cerebral amyloid angiopathy when a combination of 2 specific alleles are expressed. In addition, people with Down's syndrome, a genetic disorder, often exhibit the symptoms of Alzheimer's Disease in later life.

There are many more forms of dementia which include Vascular, Lewy body, Frontotemporal, Korsakoff's syndrome (which is related to thiamine deficiency associated with alcohol use or malnutrition), Huntington's disease, Parkinson's disease, Motor Neuron disease, Creutzfeld-Jacob disease (both sporadic and variant), dialysis dementia, and Aids-related dementia.

Dementia is predicated to increase over the next twenty years due to people living longer in society today.

To tell how Joan progressed with Alzheimer's disease I must first paint a picture of what she was like before the onset. In the film Shirley Valentine, Shirley looks into the camera and says "Why do we get all this life if we never get to use it?" Joan used her life; she worked as personal assistant for a Chartered Accountant, she loved music and enjoyed Chopin as much as Elvis Presley, ballroom dancing, fell walking and gardening. We met at Sale Locarno ballroom, married and had 3 children, Joan, James and Suzanne. Joan wanted to help the community so we became foster parents and took in 30 babies and toddlers. She always said that she had 33 children but not all by the same father. We have 6 wonderful grandchildren. She was on the Parochial Church Council; ran the church hall, doing accounts, organizing events and supervised a Mums and Tots group with up to 70 people attending. She passed her advanced driving test, became a member of The Institute of Advanced Motorists, took additional training and became an observer, was secretary of the local group, Altrincham Advanced

Motorists, and treasurer of the North West Region Liaison Committee. She was held in such high esteem by the IAM that on her death they inaugurated a road safety award in her name, "The Joan Walker Rose Bowl".

Apart from knowledge of mathematics and science, one needs logic and patience to be an engineer. Joan would constantly plan alterations and improvements to the home and my usual initial reaction was that it couldn't be done. Joan's response was that I was the engineer; "we have an engineering problem – so solve it". All in all we had a complete, happy and active life.

Using engineering logic and patience, I was able to look after Joan and devise solutions for solving some of the lifestyle problems we experienced during our journey through Alzheimer's disease.

The body viewed by an Engineer

Being a lifelong engineer, it is not surprising that I viewed the body we live in as an incredible work of engineering brilliance. The following will help to explain my solutions to Joan's motor problems described later.

As a scaffold structure the skeleton is wonderfully prepared to allow a person to meet the demands of almost every environment found on earth. There are 206 bones in the adult body, each possessing qualities of strength, flexibility, lightness, even the ability to repair and maintain itself: characteristics unlike anything mankind has been able to replicate. The bones of the body perform five main functions.

- Provide support for the body – the skeletal system provides structural support for the entire body and a framework for the attachment of soft tissues and organs.

- Protect body organs – many soft tissues and organs are surrounded by skeletal elements. For example, the rib cage protects the heart and lungs, the skull protects the brain, the vertebrae protect the spinal cord, and the pelvis protects the delicate reproductive organs.

- Provide leverage and movement – many bones function as levers that can change the magnitude and direction of the forces generated by muscles. There are different types of joints and each is appropriate for the particular function it has to perform;

1. ball and socket joint which allows for freedom of movement in several directions (e.g. femur and hipbone)

2. the hinge joint, which allows for movement in a single plane (e.g. knee and elbow)

3. the pivot joint, which allows for some freedom of movement in several directions (e.g. wrists)

4. the joints of the skull which are welded and immovable.

- Produce blood cells – red blood cells, white blood cells, and other blood elements are produced in the red marrow, which fills the internal cavities of many bones.

- Store minerals and lipids — calcium is the most abundant mineral in the body. Ninety-nine per cent of the body's calcium is found in the skeleton. The bones also store energy reserves as lipids in areas filled with yellow marrow.

Of course the bones of the body do not function in isolation. It is remarkable to contemplate the multitude of synergistic systems within the human body necessary for movement to take place.

As far as movement is concerned, one might consider the muscles which are required to contract (and equally relax) around the skeleton. This is not too dissimilar to the manner in which a puppet moves through the movement of its strings. The muscles themselves possess highly specialised tension gauges allowing them to finely respond[1] to information sent to them from our body's main computer unit – the brain, via the hard wiring of the human body – the central and peripheral nervous system. This in turn when functioning as it is designed to, allows the person to carry out a multitude of sequenced movements to achieve the desired task, from writing an essay to putting on a jacket, from driving a car to playing a game of badminton. We shouldn't for one moment forget the importance of the function of the brain to be able to process the details of the tasks in hand, a disruption of which may result in movement being compromised from minor deficiencies through to non-function.

And we must also remember that without an adequately working cardiovascular system, to breath, pump and carry oxygen, nutrients and metabolites around our bodies within the blood, a feat of engineering brilliance in itself, this most wonderful of machines that we call the human body would not even be turned on. We certainly are most wonderfully and fearfully made.

---

1. The gauges are called muscle spindles and Golgi tendon organs. They relay information to the spinal cord and brain, which then alters the fine control of the muscles via the peripheral nervous system.

The components of the brain and peripheral nervous system that process perception, thought and actions are the nerve cells, also called neurons and neurones. Many other cells in the brain perform support functions, such as the delivery of nutrients, removal of waste and protection from toxins, but the neuron comprises the core component of the mechanisms behind memory, thinking, and ultimately reasoning that forms the basis of human personality.

All animals with a nervous system have neurons; the structure and function of neurons is studied by scientists called neurophysiologists. Clinicians called Neurologists take the basic science of neurophysiology and apply it to the clinical diagnosis and treatment of diseases of the nervous system. The scientific approaches pioneered in neurophysiology may take years before they are applied to commercial medical products for the treatment of neural diseases.

Neurons work by generating electricity from the metabolism of glucose (or ketones in certain circumstances). Neurons maintain an electrical potential across a cell membrane called a resting potential. Given an appropriate trigger, the neurons change the resting potential to an action potential which then travels the length of the neuron, potentially triggering other neurons in neural networks. The frequency of the action potentials can indicate the magnitude of triggering stimulus e.g. a fast volley of action potentials could indicate a strong stimulus, a slower series of action potentials in the same neuron could indicate a much weaker stimulus. The nervous system uses a logarithmic scale of coding, and so a massive range of stimuli can be dealt with. The visual system is a good example, whereby one photon of light can be perceived after dark adaptation, and yet the same system works well on a sunny day.

Estimates vary on the number of neurons in the healthy human brain, but a low estimate is 86 billion. The complexity of neuronal networks in the brain is such that one neuron can connect to thousands of others. Just one action potential can shut down the output of another neuron, or trigger thousands of other neurons to generate many more action potentials. Out of this massive neural networking, human personality, including memory, reasoning and perception, are emergent properties. Consciousness is entirely held within the brain, it is not "beamed in" from some external point.

The functional connections between neurons in the brain are called synapses. There are two main types, electrical and chemical synapses. Electrical synapses are relatively simple electrical junctions between adjacent neurons. Chemical synapses require a neurotransmitter to be released from one neuron, which then induces an electrical response in another neuron. By altering the level of neurotransmitter at chemical synapses, many drugs are able to modulate brain function. For example, one of the drug therapies for Alzheimer's disease acts to increase the concentration of acetylcholine, a neurotransmitter, in the synapse and this helps Alzheimer's patients with some of their cognitive impairments, particularly attention. As another example, anaesthetics induce loss of consciousness to facilitate surgery by altering the efficacy of neurotransmitters at the chemical synapse. Anaesthesia is fundamentally different from natural sleep, and is known to reduce the level of brain metabolism of glucose in proportion to the depth of anaesthesia, which can be measured using equipment designed to measure the summed electrical activity of many millions of neurons at the scalp (electroencephalography = EEG).

Neurological diseases act on the nervous system by disrupting the normal functions of neurons, potentially leading to neuronal death.

Early Signs

The development of Alzheimer's disease begins so innocuously that one doesn't realize it has started. There are no check-in desks, passport controls or sign posts for this trip; if there were then early diagnosis would aid early prescription of drugs. It is only with hindsight that one sees what went on and even then the very beginning is hard to place. Denial by family is commonplace (see Elisabeth Kübler Ross later) and one can so easily explain away symptoms even though friends and neighbours ask "What is wrong with Joan?" With early age onset the task is even harder because Alzheimer's is normally associated with the elderly so someone in their 20s or 30s is likely to be diagnosed with depression or other similar malady because the symptoms are so similar. Alzheimer's begins in the brain, unlike infectious encephalopathy that enters the brain, so once the disease has compromised the brain it is too late; the drugs that are available only help with some of the symptoms in some of the patients for some of the time. When they cease to work the patient's condition and quality of life deteriorate rapidly.

Early Symptoms

From the onset of the disease I found that if I didn't react adversely to strange behaviour and treated everything as normal, then accidents, spillages and the inability to function were accepted without demur and Joan was not upset. Sometimes, in the early stages she could be a bit aggressive, get angry, probably from frustration, and strike out or throw whatever was to hand at me or at family carers. She would get confused easily with her surroundings and not recognize where she was, whether it was at home or in a restaurant.

One of the earliest symptoms that Joan presented was that she couldn't locate a stamp on an envelope correctly. I explained that the Post Office sorting machines look for the phosphor on the stamp 1cm from the edge of the envelope and to miss this area with the stamp would result in the letter being rejected. However she continued to place the stamp anywhere to the right of the address.

If she was cleaning the path, the same area would get brushed time and time again; she just couldn't move on. If we were cutting the lawn she would cut the edges but part way round would forget what she was doing and wander off to start something new. Due to the failure of her memory she would throw items away that were of sentimental value and one or other family member had to rescue it from the refuse bin.

Memories are held diffusely throughout the brain. Pioneering work on soldiers suffering head injury showed that the amount of memories lost was proportional to the amount of damage to the brain. A region of the brain known as the hippocampus is important for the acquisition and recovery of memory, and probably plays the role of an indexing system. People who have suffered specific damage to the hippocampus are unable to acquire memories after the incident.

Being Secretary of Altrincham Advanced Motorists, she would need cheques to be signed and instead of driving to the co-signatory's house she would walk; depending who she selected; this could be either 2 or 8 miles. En route she would get lost and we would have to send out a search party.

We were both active members of St Alban's Church and were elected onto the Parochial Church Council. She joined the Ladies Craft Group but after a while, having lost the coordination to sew, she just attended for the company and the tea and biscuits.

It is said that one never forgets how to ride a bike but whilst holidaying in Austria with daughter Joan's family we took a bicycle ride around a lake and discovered she had in fact forgotten. She started the ride quite steadily but as time progressed she became more and more wobbly until eventually she had to walk.

Joan loved the car and would sometimes go for a drive. Some years later, when unbeknown to us Alzheimer's had begun to affect her brain, she telephoned to say she was in Weston-Super-Mare some 175 miles away and would be staying over. She did the same thing again but on this occasion she became lost on the Wirral. Fortunately she called in at a nursing home to ask for directions. The duty manager, recognizing the symptoms, telephoned me, and with our son James, went to collect her.

Whilst on holiday in Majorca with our younger daughter, Suzanne, and her family, the stairs to our apartment were external open chequer plate which, because there were no risers, she could see through and that made her extremely nervous and reluctant to climb. At other times whilst walking through the town as a family we would suddenly notice that Joan was missing and had to search for her. On separate occasions we found her down a dark path on the sea front and in a local bar. She hated Spaghetti Bolognese but ordered the dish in a restaurant, with hindsight it must have been because she couldn't read the menu and said "I'll have the same as you". Using a knife and fork to eat was out of the question so the spaghetti had to be cut into spoon-sized pieces.

Members of the church organized a walk to Mam Tor near Castleton, Derbyshire. With our experience of fell walking it should have been an easy day out but once we left the tarmac footpath and entered the fell track the friable surface prevented her from walking. It took over an hour to negotiate 100 yards back to the metalled surface. This condition rapidly progressed to an inability even to walk on a gravel car park. I later realized that this was due to her brain not being able to process the information fed to it via the soles of her feet.

Her social behaviour altered in that when we were in the shopping centre she would sometimes approach a complete stranger and compliment them on their hair, make-up or clothes, which was totally out of character. Fortunately she was always courteous and the recipients seemed puzzled but pleased by the encounter.

We were invited to a formal annual dinner with the local Liberal Democrats party and, for no reason that we could determine, Joan remained sitting all evening with her hands clasped on her lap, not speaking, eating or drinking, much to the embarrassment of everyone at the table.

Since early in our marriage one of my domestic tasks was the ironing. However, when Joan began to find limitations in her life-style she wanted to help run the house and share the daily chores. She insisted on helping with the ironing; I had to stand with her to make sure she didn't "iron" her hand. It took the best part of 20 minutes to iron a handkerchief but when she finished I would praise her and thank her for her help.

To use the telephone became beyond her capabilities. She couldn't master all the buttons even when I marked and labelled the "Direct Dial" ones so that with one press she could connect with any of our 3 children. I had to set up the call, Joan would talk but when the conversation ended she was unable to return the handset to the cradle and just dropped it anywhere close by.

The cooker was far too complex to understand and there was always the danger of her leaving the gas on. She found making a cup of tea too much and would get confused as to how much tea, milk and water was needed.

Shortly after Suzanne and her husband separated, their wedding anniversary fell due and not remembering or not realizing that Dale had moved out Joan bought them an anniversary card.

As mentioned earlier, Joan loved dancing and well into the disease still enjoyed dancing with Suzanne to Elvis and when movement became impossible "danced with her eyes". The grandchildren danced with their Grandma and shared their soft toys; it seemed to soothe her as did watching the graceful movement of Suzanne's cat and she was so pleased and surprised when her family said they loved her.

When I retired we would start our day with a cup of tea in bed. We would just enjoy the drink and organize our day.

As time went on I would have to arrange the pillows against the headboard for her but Joan had lost the coordination to support her weight on her hands and push herself back to the headboard with her feet. The only way she could sit back was to get out of bed, walk to the head of the bed and get back in.

Some of these early symptoms were excused away as "Joan flexing her muscles and showing us who was boss" or "it's just old age creeping on". With hindsight it was neither of these but by then it was too late and the disease was already affecting her brain.

Clinical Interest

Once symptoms become more consistent, a usual approach will be to rule-out conditions that could lead to the same symptoms that are treatable.

Joan had a series of falls and in each case struck her head and needed to go to A&E for a check-up. After the first fall in the bathroom she was told that perhaps she had run up stairs too fast and it had dropped her blood pressure; she was discharged. The second time she was told it was just a one-off faint and was again discharged.

Diagnosis & Management

After the third event, A&E referred her to the Falls Clinic where a scan was taken and she was referred to the Memory Clinic where, after further tests and an MRI scan Professor Alistair Burns diagnosed Alzheimer's disease with Parkinsonian symptoms. On leaving his office Joan asked me what Alzheimer's disease was but because she was so far down the road there was no way she would understand so I explained it was a condition that made her forget things but as there were two of us we could help each other. This seemed to satisfy her curiosity.

As time went on she displayed symptoms such as muscle stiffness, fainting and falls which relate to Dementia with Lewy Bodies; inability to form words, behavioural changes and recognizing people, which relate to Frontotemporal dementia; difficulty walking and bladder problems which relate to Vascular dementia. She continued to fall periodically but later in the journey these falls were accompanied by fitting and vomiting. All of these lead me to assume that Alzheimer's disease can migrate from the occipital and parietal lobes to other areas of the brain. The image overleaf illustrates the magnitude of tissue loss due to Alzheimer's disease.

Healthy brain   **Advanced Alzheimer's**

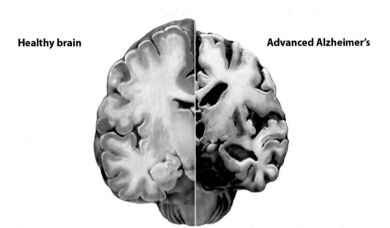

*Figure 2: A comparison between a healthy brain
and one with advanced Alzheimer's disease.*

Features of Alzheimer's Disease include:

*Deposition of β-amyloid plaques. Plaques are fibrillar deposits
of an abnormally-folded protein called amyloid β-peptide
(β-amyloid) that are found outside neurons, in the extracellular
space between brain cells. Neurofibrillar tangles are within
neurons (intracellular) and are aggregates of a protein called
tau that are normally associated with the microtubules that
form part of the structure of neurons responsible for moving
structures within the neuron. The tau protein is abnormal in
Alzheimer's disease, exhibiting chemical characteristics of
hyperphosphorylation and oxidative modification;*

Altered levels of glutamate. Glutamate is an excitatory neurotransmitter found within the brain;

Dysfunction at synapses, leading to altered or blocked messages between neurones.

To provide a diagnosis of definite Alzheimer's Disease requires post-mortem neuropathological evidence of plaques and neurofibrillary tangles.

Lewy Bodies within neurons are associated with a specific type of dementia that can overlap with the symptoms of Alzheimer's Disease. Lewy Body dementia has an increased incidence of visual disturbance and hallucination. Lewy Bodies can form early in the progression of dementia in the dorsal vagal nucleus of the brainstem, an area of the nervous system responsible for the control of vagus nerve functions including gut motility, coughing, and the modulation of heart rate.

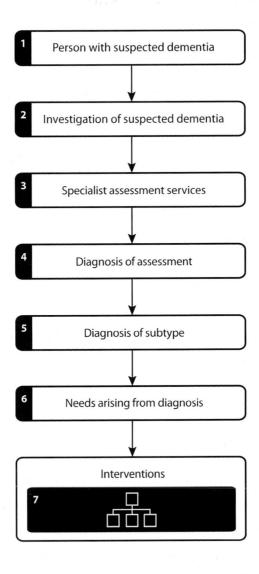

1 Person with suspected dementia

2 Investigation of suspected dementia

3 Specialist assessment services

4 Diagnosis of assessment

5 Diagnosis of subtype

6 Needs arising from diagnosis

Interventions

7

Figure 3: NICE Pathway for Dementia.

NICE recommends the following actions after diagnosis of dementia[2]:

- "make time available to discuss the diagnosis with the person with dementia and, if the person consents, with their family. Both may need ongoing support.

- offer the person with dementia and their family written information about:
  - signs and symptoms
  - course and prognosis
  - treatments
  - local care and support services
  - support groups
  - sources of financial and legal advice and advocacy
  - medico-legal issues, including driving
  - local information sources, including libraries and voluntary organisations."

Joan was a strong willed woman and steadfastly refused to see the GP. Ultimately I had to make an appointment for myself, ask Joan to accompany me and when in the consultation I would recite Joan's symptoms as my own. Even so if asked a question by the doctor she may well tell him to mind his own business. The GP prescribed Donepezil (Aricept), but quite frankly with the late diagnosis the damage to her brain was too far advanced and the drugs didn't work.

Along the way I applied for and became a Deputy of the Court of Protection in order to conduct our affairs. Fortunately before this became absolutely necessary we had arranged that all bank accounts be in joint names.

Driving created its own difficulties. If I acknowledged a courtesy from another driver she would think the person was a friend whom she had forgotten or occasionally accuse me of having other girlfriends. Joan had been a member of the IAM for over 10 years and drove to the advanced system of car control. When one is driving, whether on the motorway or on urban roads, it is normal to drive the car centrally between the white lines and the brain has learned to adjust spatial awareness accordingly. However, fairly early in the disease, Joan would position her body in the centre of the lane, which brought the nearside of the car within inches of the vehicles in the slower lane or those parked on the roadside. Similarly before overtaking she would normally do an all-round mirror check, make sure it was safe before manoeuvring. But often the mirror check was missed and she would cut-up the motorist on her off side. Driving on the Motorway became erratic with speed variations from 30 to 70 mph within the space of a few minutes on the same journey. Joan gave the excuse for poor driving that it was because I did the majority of it and she was out of practice. She would re-learn. We sat for hours in the car on the drive learning how to change gear. I ensured that the gear box was free and the lever able to go from gear to gear without starting the engine or dipping the clutch. Having to push the lever against the homing spring then forward into 1st gear was just about impossible; if she managed that then to make the straight pull back, still overcoming the tension in the spring, into 2nd gear was incredibly difficult for her. After a couple of hours I brought the gear lever back to its home position opposite 3rd and 4th so that she could engage either with a straight pull or push of the lever. This was a morale booster and satisfied her that progress was being made.

The vicar and Church Council realizing that Joan was unwell and not wishing to offend her, a stratagem was devised wherein all church activities would be controlled from the centre, which meant that the running of the Church Hall would be done by the Parish Secretary who had all the contacts for organizations and their respective bookings. Joan was not offended and it did relieve her of a great amount of stress. Similarly within Altrincham Advanced Motorists another Secretary was elected. Joan could no longer write nor sign cheques so she was quite happy with the new arrangement. I think, in the main, she didn't fully realize what was happening.

Figure 4: View of the stairwell from the highest point of the stair lift.

Negotiating stairs was the next major hurdle. To climb stairs one has to find, locate then hold the hand rail. Next, the weight and balance have to be transferred onto one foot, the toes of that foot have to spread to help with balance; the lead foot has to lift 25cm then go forward 15cm and down 2.5cm. The weight is transferred onto the upper foot, toes and balance adjusted and the body raised. The trailing foot has to lift 50cm, go forward 15cm and down 2.5cm. The weight and balance have to be adjusted yet again. When Joan was climbing stairs it was common to find that half way up she would lose executive memory, freeze and could move neither up nor down. When that happened I had to telephone our son and between us we would carry her the rest of the way. The answer to the problem seemed to be a stair lift.

One was installed and I took the first ride (toys for boys!). However when I reached the highest point my head was about 12 feet above the hall and the view down the stairwell looked like an isometric drawing with complex pattern changes in the carpet and strange angles of the banister and was totally unacceptable for someone who has their visual perception and spatial orientation compromised. I asked the engineer to remove the lift even before he had packed away his tools. The only acceptable solution was to convert the downstairs front lounge into a bedroom. The next requirement was a downstairs bathroom which was provided by building a wet room in the back of the garage with access through the utility area in the kitchen.

Figure 5: Photo taken of the completed wet room.

At this time I began to formulate plans for tasks, engineering logic if you will. I would go through the task in my mind taking into consideration the restrictions imposed by Joan's disabilities. For example, to get her into the car I tried 2 methods. Obviously the door had to be opened for her. She would steady herself by holding the top of the door with the left hand and the door frame with the right. Then bearing in mind she had to balance on the left foot, she then had to lift the right foot and put it in the black hole that was the foot-well. To get into the car she had to simultaneously turn to the left, bend at the ankle, knee, hip and back, bow the head to avoid the frame and sit on a seat that wasn't there because it was out of sight. Mission impossible! To compound the difficulty the distance between the top of the door and the seat was greater than the length of her arm and body so she couldn't reach to sit down anyway.

The second option was to open the door, stand Joan with her back to the seat, maintain eye contact and talk to her, hold her elbows and support her forearms on mine, then gently but firmly instruct her to sit. The feet then had to be lifted 30cm and at the same time she had to turn to face forwards. This movement was impossible for Joan because the dash board was smooth and there was nothing to grip to assist the manoeuvre. I had to move her myself. Lifting Joan's feet meant that she was out of control and would stiffen, causing her to roll back and lie over the driver's seat. The solution was to support her back with my right hand, lift her feet with my left and turn her to face the front of the car all in one motion. The ergonomics of the seat held her in a safe and comfortable position. Short term fear was inevitable but once strapped in we could drive off.

Eating and drinking were fraught with difficulties because to locate the cutlery when spatial awareness is compromised is nigh on impossible. The eye sees the knife and fork but the hands cannot locate or work out how to grip, coordinate and manipulate them. A spoon is easier but the damaged brain still has to load the spoon and transfer the food to the mouth. Ultimately I had to feed her myself. As time went by and her condition deteriorated, eating became more of a problem because towards the end of her journey she didn't realize she had to open her mouth to eat. I would have to blend her food anyway so that I could load the spoon, gently open her mouth with it and feed her. She had forgotten how to chew and swallow, which made things even more difficult. The tongue manipulates food for mastication and is used for speech. It also serves as a natural means of cleaning one's teeth but all these actions are under instruction from the brain. However, in Joan's case she could neither talk nor direct her tongue to clean her teeth; as a result I had to clear her mouth manually after each meal. Subsequently I had to feed her with concentrated food supplement drinks prescribed by her GP.

In the beginning, obviously, Joan would be able to use a cup or glass to drink but as time went on there were difficulties in hand-eye coordination in transferring liquid from cup to lip. To change to a drinking straw worked for a while but to drink via a straw is not straightforward; first the lips have to form an air tight seal around the straw, the nasal passages have to close then the tongue and cheeks have to reposition to create a partial vacuum in the mouth so that atmospheric air pressure, which is the weight of the column of air from sea level up to the stratosphere and is approximately

15 pounds per square inch (1000 millibars), bearing down on the surface of the liquid can force it up the straw. One does not suck the fluid; it is the differential between the outside pressure and the reduction within the mouth that causes the transfer. After a while Joan could not use a straw and we had to change to a disability drinking mug with a spout. As with the straw the same applies to breathing; we do not suck air into the lungs. The brain tells the diaphragm to move downwards, this creates a partial vacuum in the chest and atmospheric pressure forces air into the lungs. This is why climbers on Everest have difficulty breathing because they are so high there is no air pressure to fill the lungs. When a patient loses this faculty, as can happen with advanced Alzheimer's disease, then a ventilator would be needed to assist with breathing.

Before Joan became incontinent, she would sit on the toilet but nothing would happen, she would become very upset, ask me what to do to make it work and plead with me to do it for her, which of course was impossible. I tried to explain which muscles to relax and which to use to push but obviously the concept was quite outside her ability to comprehend let alone apply. This became very distressing for me because of the sheer frustration at not being able to help. This interim period was very awkward because Joan would have accidents but because she was not fully incontinent she wasn't wearing the full pads and her normal clothes became soiled.

When she eventually became incontinent she wore the proper appliances. As I cleaned her, taking care to clean from front to back to reduce the risk of infection, I would chat about anything rather than the job in hand so as to make it an ordinary everyday occurrence that happened to everyone at some time or another.

Moving from room to room became difficult; she could look at the lounge door and not be able to open it. Doors could be difficult because she had to work out if the door was hinged on the left or right, did it open outwards or inwards, if inwards where should she stand to avoid obstructing it as it opened. Once the door was opened, there were problems moving from room to room; if the floor covering or décor was different and there was a carpet strip across the threshold with visual perception compromised Joan's brain could not process the information it was receiving through her eyes and rationalize that it was still safe. Over time this meant that to move her around the house I had to sit her in a wheel chair, tuck her hands inside the chair, hold the chair arms and propel her through the door backwards. By the time she realized she was in another room it was too late and the new room then became the norm and the same stratagem used to exit.

Figure 6: shower and visual barriers.

The same problems arose in the bathroom. I changed all the basin taps from standard screw down to quarter turn long lever design. This extended Joan's independence and helped for a while. She couldn't balance on one foot to raise the other to get over the rim and into the bath; she was also frightened that if she managed to get in she would not be able to get out. I had the bath replaced with a disability shower tray but once again the change in colour and texture created its own difficulties. To help with stability and to reassure Joan I fitted grab rails around the toilet and shower.

There were three barriers that had to be negotiated between bedroom and shower: bedroom to landing, landing to bathroom and finally over the edge of the shower tray. These obstacles would have been impossible to overcome without the assistance of a wheeled shower chair. The low tray and half doors allowed me to shower Joan from outside the cubicle. To shower her I had to keep the water flow rate very gentle and the temperature warm, start at the feet and work my way up so that it reduced sensory shocks to a minimum.

Figure 7: Visual barriers from bedroom to shower tray.

To wash her hair I would sit her with her back to the kitchen sink (it was higher than the wash-basin in the bathroom) and with her head tilted back, her hair could be washed without getting water or shampoo on her face.

The semantic part of her brain began to deteriorate and instead of forming speech she produced a series of loud explosive sounds – da da da da! This inability to string words together properly resulted in another form of communication, irritation and aggression. I found that economy of words helped with communication and I soon discovered that, with Joan, I should not ask questions. For example if I was to ask her for her name and she couldn't remember then not knowing one's name is a traumatic event because it is a loss of something that is an intrinsic part of one's being. Even remembering the day of the week is reliant on remembering what day it was yesterday or remembering having heard it on the radio or television. I didn't even ask if she wanted a drink; I would brew up and if she was thirsty she would drink, if not she wouldn't. What had I lost? Perhaps a cup of tea.

At the onset of the disease I couldn't understand why Joan, who obviously had been dressing and undressing herself for over 60 years, suddenly found the process extremely complicated. The easiest way to help was to dress her as one would a child. I would start by sitting her on the bed and pulling her underwear above her knees. Then each trouser leg was gathered independently and also pulled above the knee. By holding both garments by the waist band and using the clothes as a sling I could lift her into a standing position, at the same time pulling both up to her waist. The bra is the most difficult piece of clothing ever invented; it is like three pieces of flimsy string with no shape or substance. To try to put it on from the front was to invite Joan to grasp one or other of the straps, which she refused to release. To fasten it first and pull it round the body meant that the arms had to perform very tight manoeuvres, which proved extremely difficult. If I tried to help her she would lock her arms close to the body. After a while I abandoned the bra altogether.

Crew neck and tight tops had to be avoided because to obstruct the eyes and to pull the garment over the face proved very traumatic. Even with a wide neck the arm mobility was restricted because Joan didn't understand what I was trying to do and would freeze which made getting the arm into the sleeve more or less impossible. Button-through blouses and cardigans were better but even then care had to be taken.

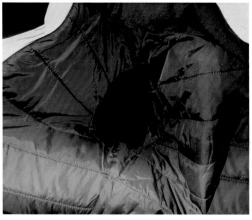

Figure 8: Rabbit hole and a sleeve hole.

Imagine being asked to put your hand into a rabbit warren; most people would refuse because one never knew what might be lurking down there, perhaps a snake or fox or even an aggressive rabbit. By the same token, to ask someone with Alzheimer's disease, whose visual perception is impaired, to put their hand into the black hole that was a sleeve carried the same fears. With Joan the only problem-free method was to present the garment, whether it was a cardigan, blouse or coat, from the rear, guide her hands into the sleeves and lift it onto her shoulders ready to fasten from the front.

Such fear could be due to a centre in the brain called the amygdala, which is responsible for storing the emotional and physiological state during a traumatic incident and recalling the associated fear as a protective mechanism should the circumstances start to arise again. It is plausible that the lack of higher brain reasoning due to atrophy of frontal lobes could lead a person to be fearful of situations due to activity by the amygdala that to others would be understood and the fear dismissed.

Joan's brain sent inappropriate signals to her bladder so that she imagined it needed emptying every few minutes throughout the day and night. At the same time she may well go into a full body spasm. For ease of access and not to have to make the journey to the bathroom we used a commode in the bedroom. This enabled me to lift her out of bed and just turn her through 90° whenever she had the urge to go. On a good night I would have to toilet her 5 or 6 times, a normal night might be double that, on a bad night I could well be up all night. Often I would get her settled but before I could return to my side of the bed she would ask for the toilet. This 24 hour attention caused me to suffer from sleep deprivation. This is a very strange place; it is as though the brain has been removed from the body and is floating nearby but there are no connections between the two and the brain is trying to control a body to which is not connected. My family thought the work load was too dangerous for me to continue so we visited Nursing Homes, found one that was acceptable, paid a deposit and signed the contract. However that night I was up again as usual with Joan and as often happened she went into a full body spasm. To lift her I had to turn her across the bed and perform a dead weight lift, something every physiotherapist would advise against but there was no option. When I had her upright and was holding her close I just lost control and wept; I don't know how long I stood there with her. She was vulnerable, frail and utterly dependant and I knew I couldn't give her over to strangers no matter how caring and dedicated they might be. I cancelled the contract. Having to work a night shift then a day shift then a night shift without respite was debilitating to say the least. I was strong enough both mentally and physically to look after her. Not everyone is this fortunate and my heart goes out to those who cannot cope and have to place their loved ones in care. It must be devastating. The decision to keep Joan at home sort of evolved up to this point but it was influenced by my own mother's situation when, due to unavoidable circumstances, she had to go into a home.

She hated it and repeatedly asked to leave. When she died she was with carers but not her family and I vowed that I would do everything I could to prevent Joan from experiencing such an end. The caring slowly turned into nursing and I don't know the day or month when it happened, it was a way of living that slowly changed to accommodate her emerging disabilities.

Joan began to forget who people were; recognition of those nearest and dearest to her was lost, yet on rare occasions her eyes and face would light up when I came into view and the most beautiful smile would illuminate her face; sadly it was gone in a trice. She didn't recognise her own children and grandchildren. She didn't know who they were but she seemed to know that they loved her and would care for her. To help her remember her family and friends I compiled a small photo album with their images. Every day I would sit with her and we would go through the photos and reminisce about the occasions when they were taken. Children and grandchildren would show photos on the computer and give her soft toys to hold which seemed to both stimulate and comfort for a while, but tragically her brother, sister and even her children and grandchildren became strangers.

She had become reliant on me as her main carer and even if our children were with her and I left the room to make a drink she would become very agitated until I returned.

Likewise if she had a sleep in the afternoon I had to place myself in a position so that when she opened her eyes I was the first person she saw.

To communicate with Joan I needed to use:

1. Short simple sentences and speak slowly

2. Try not to ask questions because for her to answer required memory

3. Talk about one thing at a time using facial expressions and gestures

4. Be patient and understanding

5. Use a proper tone of voice

6. Use eye contact at all times

7. Repeat back a sentence allowing her to know I was listening, and to encourage further communication.

People sometimes say that Alzheimer's disease is like a second childhood but nothing could be further from the truth. A child loves to have its nappy changed but a person with an incontinent pad is ashamed. A child is a growing person; someone with Alzheimer's is disintegrating and cannot relearn what is lost. It is so easy for someone with Alzheimer's disease to lose their dignity because of all the associated loss of function, but, as with Joan, I realized that she would only lose her dignity if I stopped treating her with dignity.

Some of the attributes I had to develop to do my job were empathy, patience, respect, acceptance, reliability and self-awareness. In people with dementia sometimes their only way of communicating is through their behaviour.

Joan developed a bowel blockage but was not strong enough to attend a day clinic for tests so had to go into hospital for MRI and ultrasound scans and X-Rays to identify the problem. She became too traumatised to stay in an alien room with all the equipment on her own and was unable to stay still long enough for an X-ray to be taken or to go through the scanner on her own. I was equipped with a lead-lined, protective coat that allowed me to hold her in position for the X-ray and to go partway through the scanner with her. Ovarian Cancer was diagnosed and she was given 4-6 months to live.

She was in hospital for 3 weeks and during that time lost over a stone in weight. When I telephoned each morning for an overnight report I was always told she had a good quiet night. But one day when I visited she had been moved into a private room, the other patients told me it was because she made so much noise shouting and screaming that she disturbed others. From then on I attended hospital for at least 12 hours each day so that I could feed and bathe her. The nurses could neither bathe nor shower her due to the danger of full body spasms, which made even a hoist too dangerous to use in case she slipped out and because of Health and Safety Regulations. I had to shower her in the ward bathroom. Joan would protest and fill the ward with her screams but afterwards was grateful to feel fresh and clean. When Joan was admitted to hospital she could stand and walk short distances but after 3 weeks in bed when even the physiotherapists would not get her to her feet to exercise, again because of Health and Safety Regulations, she became bedfast.

The local Community Nurse provided a hospital bed at home, which I had installed in the lounge against the patio doors to enable Joan to look out over the garden. I slept on a camp bed next to her so that I was to hand in case she needed me during the night. The Alzheimer's symptoms became more severe; she couldn't move and because of her disabilities some tasks required 2 people and I had to employ carers who came in 4 times a day for about 15 minutes each visit to give her a bed bath, change her clothes and bedding. To wash her hair we bought an inflatable head bath, which made the job so easy and comfortable for Joan. We removed the pillows, laid her head in the bath; when finished the bath water drained into a bowl under the bed. To weigh Joan for the GP and District Nurse's records, James would weigh himself on the bathroom scales, pick up his Mum and get back on the scales. We then subtracted one from the other to calculate her weight.

Joan, James and Suzanne, our three children, supported me for the duration of the disease by sitting with their Mum and taking over the caring so that I could go out for a coffee or shopping or just catch up on a little sleep. On top of this help any decision I made as regards their Mum's life and treatment was accepted and supported without question, which was a fantastic boost to my morale.

After diagnosis the Occupational Health staff made a survey of our home and recommended minor adaptations to help with movement and safety. They also provided the hospital bed and pressure relief mattress and pump. The District Nurse visited every week. We received wonderful support from our GP, Dr Karen Drabble, who had nominated herself within the Practice as Joan's main carer and initially visited every other week. When she was off duty Dr Robert Jenyo was there with much needed support. Towards the end Dr Drabble doubled her visits so as to monitor medication and to offer any help that I might need. She also insisted on issuing the Death Certificate.

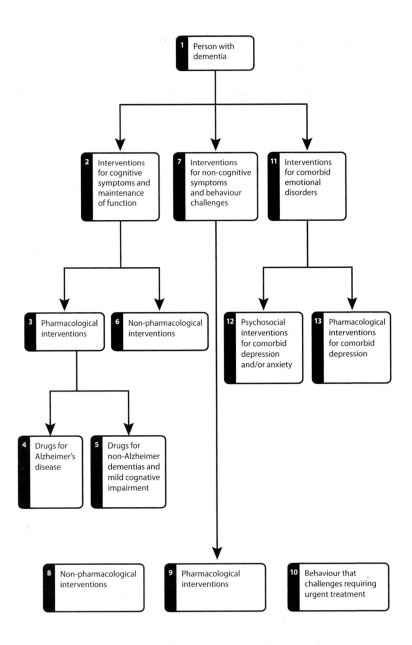

Figure 9: NICE Intervention Pathway.

During her last few days she was unable to take any nourishment and all I could do for her was to moisten her lips and squeeze fluid into her mouth using a small sponge. She couldn't talk but over the years I had learned to read her needs from the expression in her eyes, her mouth or body language and I knew if Joan had to be moved to ease pressure points, or needed Oramorph for the pain, which I could administer using a measuring syringe.

NICE recommended drugs for Alzheimer's disease: Donepezil, galantamine, rivastigmine and memantine.

1. *The three acetylcholinesterase (AChE) inhibitors donepezil, galantamine and rivastigmine are recommended as options for managing mild to moderate Alzheimer's disease under all of the conditions specified in paragraphs 3 and 4 below.*

2. *Memantine is recommended as an option for managing Alzheimer's disease for people with: moderate Alzheimer's disease who are intolerant of or have a contraindication to AChE inhibitors or severe Alzheimer's disease. Treatment should be under the conditions specified in paragraph 3.*

3. *Treatment should be under the following conditions: Only specialists in the care of patients with dementia (that is, psychiatrists including those specialising in learning disability, neurologists, and physicians specialising in the care of older people) should initiate treatment.*

Carers' views on the patient's condition at baseline should be sought. Treatment should be continued only when it is considered to be having a worthwhile effect on cognitive, global, functional or behavioural symptoms. Patients who continue on treatment should be reviewed regularly using cognitive, global, functional and behavioural assessment. Treatment should be reviewed by an appropriate specialist team, unless there are locally agreed protocols for shared care. Carers' views on the patient's condition at follow-up should be sought.

4. *If prescribing an AChE inhibitor (donepezil, galantamine or rivastigmine), treatment should normally be started with the drug with the lowest acquisition cost (taking into account required daily dose and the price per dose once shared care has started). However, an alternative AChE inhibitor could be prescribed if it is considered appropriate when taking into account adverse event profile, expectations about adherence, medical comorbidity, possibility of drug interactions and dosing profiles.*

5. *When using assessment scales to determine the severity of Alzheimer's disease, healthcare professionals should take into account any physical, sensory or learning disabilities, or communication difficulties that could affect the results and make any adjustments they consider appropriate. Healthcare professionals should also be mindful of the*

need to secure equality of access to treatment for patients from different ethnic groups, in particular those from different cultural backgrounds.

6. *When assessing the severity of Alzheimer's disease and the need for treatment, healthcare professionals should not rely solely on cognition scores in circumstances in which it would be inappropriate to do so. These include: if the cognition score is not, or is not by itself, a clinically appropriate tool for assessing the severity of that patient's dementia because of the patient's learning difficulties or other disabilities (for example, sensory impairments), linguistic or other communication difficulties or level of education or if it is not possible to apply the tool in a language in which the patient is sufficiently fluent for it to be appropriate for assessing the severity of dementia or if there are other similar reasons why using a cognition score, or the score alone, would be inappropriate for assessing the severity of dementia. In such cases healthcare professionals should determine the need for initiation or continuation of treatment by using another appropriate method of assessment. These recommendations are from Donepezil, galantamine, rivastigmine and memantine for the treatment of Alzheimer's disease (review) (NICE technology appraisal guidance 217). NICE has written information for patients and the public explaining the guidance on drugs for Alzheimer's disease.*

Other medication:

Movicol for constipation

Latanoprost eye drops for Glaucoma.

Risperidone 1mg/ml 0.3ml twice per day, can go up to 0.5ml twice per day. To prevent agitation.

Amitriptyline – antidepressant

Diazepam 5ml at night. Anti-spasmodic and to help sleep

Buprenorphine 10μg/hour patch. Changed every Tuesday. For pain relief.

Joan lost the ability to swallow tablets so I had to withdraw Asprin, Calcichew and Donepezil (Aricept).

The only antibiotics to which she had no adverse reaction were: Cefalexin capsules and Cefuroxime iv 1.5g.

Unacceptable drugs to which she was allergic: Clarythromycim, Nitrofurantoin, Citalopram, Sulfamethoxazole, Trimethoprim, Doxycycline and all Penicillin based drugs.

Simvastatin caused pain in her bones.

On the last day of her journey, we had friends to visit; I was talking with them at one end of the lounge when, out of nowhere, there was no sound or movement but I knew something was wrong. I asked our friends to leave, went to Joan, held her in my arms and as I talked to her I watched the pulse at the base of her neck. It gently slowed and finally stopped. It was as if Our Lord had come down, gathered her in His arms and taken her home. It was one of the most beautiful experiences of my life. She died at 3.45 in the afternoon of July 14th 2010.

Coping and the Future

I have already mentioned our three children and six grandchildren. They all live within 10 minutes' walk so all six grandchildren saw the deterioration of their Grandma at first hand. The disease was explained to them in general terms but along the lines that Grandma was becoming forgetful due to her brain being poorly. Eventually her brain would forget to tell her heart to beat and she would die and go to live with her Mum and Dad and Jesus in heaven.

Along this journey I experienced many mixed emotions, not least anger. Not anger at Joan but anger at the disease that was slowly killing everything that made her a person. On occasions I had to stop what I was doing and go into another room, punch a pillow or cushion or scream and scream until I was black in the face. Others relieved the stress with tears. This, I am told, is a normal reaction. When the screaming was over and I had "blown the safety valve" I was able to return to her care with the gentleness she deserved.

Some emotions are part of grieving and can occur during the long journey from normality to the mental and emotional death of a loved one. At the end what remains is an empty shell with a beating heart. Eventually the body dies and normal grieving will take its course. The emotions I experienced were explained by Elisabeth Kübler Ross, a Swiss-American psychiatrist who was a pioneer in near-death studies; Denial, Anger, Bargaining, Depression and Acceptance. All these feelings are part of grieving and will be felt by the patient as well as the carer.

These five stages of grieving helped me to understand what was going on even though there was little I could do to alleviate the situation.

1. Denial is a conscious or unconscious refusal to accept facts, information, reality, etc., relating to the situation concerned. It's a defence mechanism and perfectly natural. Some people can become locked in this stage when dealing with a traumatic change that can be ignored. Death of course is not particularly easy to avoid or evade indefinitely.

2. Anger can manifest in different ways. People dealing with emotional upset can be angry with themselves, and/ or with others, especially those close to them. Knowing this helps keep one detached and non-judgemental when experiencing the anger of someone who is very upset.

3. Bargaining. Traditionally the bargaining stage for people facing death can involve attempting to bargain with whatever God the person believes in. People facing less serious trauma can bargain or seek to negotiate a compromise. For example "Can we still be friends?" when facing a break-up. Bargaining rarely provides a sustainable solution, especially if it's a matter of life or death.

4. Depression. Also referred to as preparatory grieving. In a way it's the dress rehearsal or the practice run for the 'aftermath' although this stage means different things depending on whom it involves. It's a sort of acceptance with emotional attachment. It's natural to feel sadness and regret, fear, uncertainty, etc. It shows that the person has at least begun to accept the reality.

5. Acceptance. Again this stage definitely varies according to the person's situation, although broadly it is an indication that there is some emotional detachment and objectivity. People dying can enter this stage a long time before the people they leave behind, who must necessarily pass through their own individual stages of dealing with the grief.

No one should have to make the journey through Alzheimer's disease, neither as a patient nor as a carer. Joan's journey is over but mine goes on. I still have periods when I say to myself "What if" or "if only", but the only thing that would have helped was early diagnosis and drugs that actually worked. I am 76 years old and with 10 years intimate experience of Alzheimer's disease behind me, rather than turn my back on it I have decided to do what I can to raise awareness and hopefully funds for research by working as a Volunteer Champion of Alzheimer's Research UK on the basis that it is more productive to diagnose and prevent this disease than budget to support the increasing thousands of sufferers and their families in the community. My sincere wish is that shortly there may be early diagnosis and the development of preventative drugs. I remember the Poliomyelitis epidemics of the late 1940s and early 50s when a big robust friend contracted the disease and within months he was on crutches and his legs were reduced to matchsticks. He was one of the lucky ones, he survived. Now, a few drops of Sabin's vaccine on a sugar cube taken as a child can afford complete protection. This is what I pray for as regards Alzheimer's Disease. I am not suggesting for one moment that care in the community is not needed, it is essential for those in need.

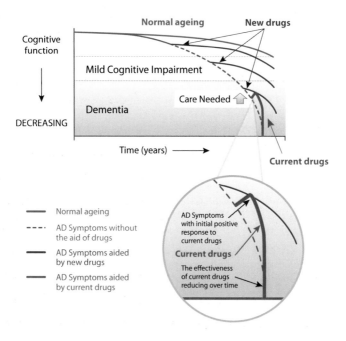

Illustration redrawn from original by Dr Eric Karran.

As one can see from the graphs if preventative drugs, or drugs to delay symptoms, are administered early enough then the onset of the disease could be pushed back beyond the normal age of life expectancy and the disease would not exist. If the symptoms were delayed by just five years the number of patients would be reduced by 50%. The graphs show that current drugs have some but only marginal affect. To look for a cure and replace the lost tissue that had carried a lifetime of memories, experiences and abilities, i.e. the life of the patient, would mean that any replacement tissue would not contain those attributes. The patient would have to start again from scratch to store a new life, new memories and new experiences in the new "empty" cells and would not be the same person that originally developed the disease.

I took early retirement which unbeknown to either of us gave us an extra 10 years together before Alzheimer's began its inexorable attack on her brain. Joan and I became regular customers at a Starbucks store where the staff watched her deterioration with great sadness. After her death they asked if they could do something to support her memory and we organized a sponsored climb of Snowdon. Thirteen of us, members of Starbucks and my family completed the climb and raised over £2300. That was in 2011. In 2012 three generations of my family; my son James, daughter Suzanne, grandson Stephen and I together with a family friend undertook a sponsored free fall sky dive from 14,000 feet and raised a further £2500. During all this time I was, and still am, on the speaker's list for Probus, Round Table, Rotary and various clubs and church groups where in raising awareness of this terrible disease I also manage to raise funds for Alzheimer's Research UK.

I include this poem which paints a graphic picture of the journey through Alzheimer's disease and is written by Margaret MacKinlay and dedicated to her sister-in-law Mary. It was composed using Mary's own words.

"ME"

"There are still many things I can do,
like walking, smiling, crying, laughing, speaking my way.
I am here and I hear you speak. I have not yet gone.

My mind might be slowly ebbing away
but deep down I know I am still Mary.
You see the changes in me I do not.
I have not yet gone.

I know the time will come
when I will not remember your name but please remind me,
so that even for a few seconds
I can say it back to you. I have not yet gone.

When words fail me I strike out.
I do not mean to hurt you.
I still have feelings but these feelings I cannot put into words.
I have not yet gone.

Actions speak louder than words.
Your help keeps me going. I have not yet gone.

Where have you gone?
I know not where.
When I call you, you do not answer.
Where am I?
I am not sure but in my world I feel secure.
I have not yet gone.

I love your smile, your name has gone.
I know your face and feel at peace.
I have not yet gone."

Joan's funeral was attended by over 150 mourners; members of Joan's family, friends, neighbours, parishioners, ex-police officers, a Trafford Councillor, nurses, care workers and members of the Institute of Advanced Motorists. The Rev Helen Scarisbrick officiated, assisted by the Rev John Beaney who read the Eulogy and the Rev John Boyers who delivered the Bible readings; Psalm 139 vs 1 – 18 and 1 Corinthians 13: vs 1 – 13. The coffin was carried by my son James and me, assisted by 2 members of staff from the Funeral Directors. A reception and lunch were held at the Cresta Court Hotel, Altrincham.

I wrote the following Eulogy for Joan.

Fred and the family would like to thank you all for giving of your time to join us to say goodbye to Joan and to celebrate her life. We have family, friends, neighbours, Joan's medical team and her Carers with us. It's a testament to the love and affection in which she was held that so many are here today.

Joan enjoyed watching old films and one of her favourites was "Shirley Valentine". In one scene Shirley says "Why do we get all this life if we don't ever use it?" Joan used every second of hers and most of it was in helping others.

She went to Navigation Road Primary School and then on to Wellington Road. During her school years her parents bought 4 shops in Bowdon Vale, a newsagents, grocers, hardware and a bakery so before school Joan would deliver papers and after school would work in the shops. After selling the shops they moved to Haddon Grove, Timperley.

She worked for a short time at Budenburg's Factory as a clerk but not enjoying the experience left and joined Eric Dickinson, a Chartered Accountant in Altrincham – she loved it and eventually became his PA. She liked nothing better than to find the imbalances and compensating errors needed to balance the books.

She enjoyed ballroom dancing and it was at Sale Locarno that she met Fred. They courted, married on the 1st August 1964 and had three children; Joan, James and Suzanne. While bringing up her own children she continued to work at home on accounts to help with the family budget but this was not enough for Joan so she and Fred became Foster Parents. One day Joan was pushing one of the foster children in her pram when a neighbour, who had not seen Joan for some time, stopped to congratulate her on her new baby, looked into the pram and was confronted by a little black face. Joan of course said nothing, leaving the neighbour to come to her own conclusions. Eventually people would say "How many children have you had – the reply would be 33 but not all by the same father!" Mostly they were new-born and she would look after them until they went on to their adoptive parents. Some were abused mentally and physically and one or two had severe medical problems. One in particular was delivered to the house by a nurse, the baby was 3 months old and weighed 4lb 9ozs and as the nurse left she said "Don't worry if she dies over the week end, we'll know it wasn't your fault". No pressure there then! The baby lived, had heart surgery and now has 2 strapping lads of her own. All the children were unwanted, but with Joan's capacity for love they would leave content, complete and secure.

She enjoyed camping and caravanning. Our first family holiday was in Cornwall with Joan's Mum and Dad on a farmer's field; later three carloads of us went on a camping tour of France. When in the Yorkshire Dales on a rainy day Joan persuaded us to go for a walk in swimming cozzies and wellies. On a later holiday in France she caught her first trout. She was so excited that she whipped the fish out of the water so fast it was like an Exocet Missile, it performed a perfect arc over her head and landed in a lady's hat behind her. She saw the glaciers on Mont Blanc bathed in the evening sun so that it glowed like an enormous pink ice cream. She loved the countryside, climbed Cader Idris, Snowdon and Kinder Scout. She enjoyed holidaying in Tenerife and went to Australia with Fred and her sister Anita to meet her brother Leslie where she paddled in the Pacific, saw iguanas, wallabies, kangaroo and crocodile but for some reason she wouldn't share a crocodile pie with Fred for lunch. Her sense of adventure was wonderful to behold. We were sailing back from Sicily to Malta on her brother Leslie's boat when we lost power in a Force 6 gale. Joan lay on the bench and took in the beauty of the Milky Way without a qualm or fear. She said that if God wanted her she was ready to go.

We joined St Alban's in 1965 and typically Joan had to get involved. She became a member of the PCC, ran the Church Hall, organized working parties, did the accounts, bookings and led the Mums and Tots with gatherings of up to 70.

Our son James persuaded her to become an Advanced Motorist, which she did, became an observer, joined the committee and for many years was the Group Secretary.

Joan dearly loved her children, Joan, James and Suzanne and the grandchildren, Stephen, Joanna, Joshua, Daniel, Abigail and Ethan. Family came first and the house was always full of love and laughter when we came together for birthdays and Christmas. She enjoyed being pampered by Suzanne who did her hair, nails and makeup while listening to Elvis. To be called "Granny Annie" by the grandchildren would invoke a chase around the garden.

We all have fond memories of Joan so occasionally please bring them out, dust them off, enjoy them and keep them safe.

And finally, Fred has this to say: on reflection, having been allowed to nurse Joan for three years is an honour and a privilege. She stayed at home, which is where she wanted to be.

To hold her and talk to her while she slipped peacefully into Our Lord's arms was the most beautiful thing I have ever experienced. I'm glad it's me here this morning rather than Joan, because I would hate for her to feel the pain I feel today.

Thank you. God bless you and keep you safe. Amen.

Exactly 46 years to the hour after her Dad gave her to me in marriage I returned her to him. I buried her ashes in the Garden of Remembrance under the tree where her Mum and Dad's ashes lie at 2.00 p.m. on 1st August 2010. Our family had grown from 2 to 14 in that time and we all met to say goodbye. All her life Joan had said that "we don't cry in public" but this is easier said than done and on her death, funeral and internment of her ashes some of us were overcome by the occasion. In the main we mourned in private just as she would have wished.

In conclusion, Joan and I had a lifestyle that was normal. Problems arose and normal changed, it became more difficult but one adapts until the new situation became normal and so it went on forever changing and evolving as the disease spread through her brain. Normal continued to get harder and escalated to a new level but in every case one adapts again and again as normal becomes more and more difficult so that by the time we arrived at the end of the journey and looked back I wondered how I'd managed to cope.

At the beginning of the journey I described myself as "an ordinary bloke" but along the way I learned caring and nursing skills; for 10 years I had to live with the pain and the emotional rollercoaster. I am now a different person, stronger and in some respect more patient but at the same time able to recognize what is important and what is irrelevant. Joan and I married in church in 1964 and the words of the marriage ceremony say, inter alia "from this day forward, for better for worse, for richer for poorer, in sickness and in health, till death us do part" and those words are part of a contract, not just between Joan and me, but also between God and me because I was contracted to look after one of His creatures. I'm glad I made the journey with Joan; looking back, I wouldn't have missed it for the world because I know I did a good job and was able to ease her passage.

The best prospect is to find drugs that prevent the onset of the disease. After that, a drug that slows down the progression of the disease. A reliable, non-invasive test that can detect the disease at the earliest possible time would greatly assist the clinical trials needed to perform delay of onset studies, and moreover would provide patients with clarity.

By stopping the degeneration of the brain early, brain function and the ability to lead an independent life could be preserved.

References

1. *http://www.patient.co.uk/doctor/Wernicke-Korsakoff-Syndrome.htm.*
   Accessed 07 April 2013

2. *Dementia diagnosis and assessment. NICE Pathways.*
   Dementia pathway Copyright © NICE 2013.
   Pathway last updated: 02 April 2013.
   Available at www.nice.org.uk

3. *Dementia interventions. NICE Pathways.*
   Dementia pathway Copyright © NICE 2013.
   Pathway last updated: 02 April 2013
   Available at www.nice.org.uk

To help defeat dementia please visit:
www.alzheimersresearchuk.org/donate-to-us/

Alzheimer's Research UK
3 Riverside, Granta Park
Cambridge CB21 6AD
Direct line: 01223 824567   Mobile: 07500 119514
www.alzheimersresearchuk.org

Twitter @ARUKnews
Facebook www.facebook.com/alzheimersresearchuk

Registered charity nos. 1077089 and SC042474

Dementia Care in the Community

Dementia has a huge impact on someone's life, as well as on their families and carers. There is practical and emotional support available to help people with dementia and those helping to care for them.

Accessing services and support can make a big positive difference to someone with dementia and their family. Some services will be provided by local authorities, and others can be arranged through GPs. For advice, contact your local authority social services department. The number will be in the phone book. Everyone with dementia should be entitled to an assessment that establishes their needs and suggests how those needs can be met.

Helpful contact numbers

The following organisations provide information, support and care services to people with dementia as well as their families and carers.

Admiral Nursing DIRECT is a telephone helpline, provided by Admiral Nurses and supported by the charity Dementia UK. It offers practical advice and emotional support to people with dementia on **0845 257 9406**.

The **Age UK** advice line, **0800 169 6565**, provides information about help available through social services, as well as advice about other issues faced by older people.

Alzheimer Scotland provides the National Dementia Helpline **0808 808 3000** in Scotland as well as local services all over Scotland for people with dementia and their carers.

Alzheimer's Society provides the National Dementia Helpline in England and Wales on **0300 222 1122** which offers information, support, guidance and signposting to other appropriate organisations. In Northern Ireland call **028 9066 4100**.

The Carers Trust works to improve support, services and recognition for anyone living with the challenges of caring, unpaid, for a family member or friend who is ill, frail disabled or has mental health or addiction problems. **www.carers.org**

Guideposts Trust run the Dementia Information Service for Carers. Its National Information Line is **0845 120 4048** and provides information, advice and support to carers.

The Lewy Body Society, in partnership with Parkinson's UK, provides support and advice to people with Dementia with Lewy bodies, their families and carers. You can contact a helpline advisor on **0808 800 0303**.

The **NHS** provides free, confidential information and advice for carers through Carers Direct on **0808 802 0202**.

officers, and Buchan was going to have to let him know that the nave was no longer a film set, but a crime scene. Whatever authority Oscar had had the previous day, was no longer extant.

'Oscar?'

'The line producer,' said Oscar.

'I don't know what that means,' said Buchan.

Oscar looked exasperated. There was a loud noise behind them, something being knocked over, and he swirled with an exclamation of, 'Jesus Christ,' then he turned back, still agitated, it not being apparent what had made the noise.

'I don't know what that means,' repeated Buchan.

Oscar, still under the delusion he held any power in the room, looked annoyed at Buchan's lack of insider filmmaking knowledge and said, 'I run this. *This*. This film set, right here.' He made a sweeping gesture around the nave. 'And now your people are trampling all over the damn thing. Jerry's going to be here in like half an hour, then Caroline'll be in at some point, and holy shit, they are going to *explode*. I need you people gone by,' and he looked at his watch, 'seven-forty-five. Eight o'clock at the latest. But really, we need this place cleared.'

Buchan held his gaze, as though he might have been able to communicate unspoken to him just how ridiculous he was sounding.

'What?'

'Someone's been murdered,' said Buchan.

'I know. But really, that's nothing to do with our shoot. We have nothing to contribute here. You can't, you know, you can't just come in here and trample all over literally everything because some guy fell on a stick.'

'No one fell on a stick,' said Buchan. 'There's been a murder. There is no shoot. Not today. Not tomorrow. Unlikely to be happening again any time soon.'

'No, no, nope, no, nope, nope, not happening,' he said, finger wagging in Buchan's face. 'Just no, not happening. This is our space. Has been for a fortnight, will be for the rest of this week, *and* next week. This place is doubling for like three different locations, our shoot is entirely dependent on it. This cannot be happening. I get you need to do your jobs, but you know, we've all seen the shows, we've all seen what goes on. You've got about fifty people in here. You sweep the room, you take the corpse away, the bulk of the work is then done in labs and sterilized rooms. That's all you need. You don't need to shut

—

9

us down.'

You talk a lot for someone with nothing to contribute, thought Buchan, and he hadn't yet got anywhere near asking any questions.

'I mean, look at the light in this damned city,' said Oscar.

'You've got giant searchlights outside, pointed at the windows,' said Buchan. 'Isn't that your daylight?'

'I mean, seriously? Have you the slightest understanding of film set lighting? Look, sorry, I didn't catch it. What even are you? Sergeant, detective? Like, who am I even speaking to? Do you have a senior officer?'

Oscar turned away briefly, spotted a scenes of crime officer closely examining a large ARRI ALEXA 35 camera, and barked something indistinct across the nave in his direction, being ignored in turn.

'Oscar,' said Buchan, 'we've set up a room through here. You need to come and talk.'

5

'You know how long it takes to get a movie like this going? I mean, have you any idea?'

Buchan was in the ad hoc interview room, next to the church vestry, with Caroline Tennyson, the director of the movie. She instantly appreciated the situation much better than Oscar, the line producer. Perhaps, thought Buchan, Oscar had been playing a part. He needed to act like he was still able to do his job. He needed to be seen to be bold and direct and wanting to get on with it, so that he'd be in a good position for his next gig. None of this was his fault, he'd done everything he could. Or perhaps he was just entitled, with an absurd sense of the film's importance.

Tennyson, on the other hand, had known the movie shoot was over from the minute she'd taken Oscar's call that morning, her questions to Buchan delivered in a tired, long-suffering tone.

'You have no studio money behind you?' asked Buchan, playing along, using his small amount of movie production knowledge, the way he might've said, 'S'il vous plaît,' in a Parisian café, while hoping the waiter did not respond in French.

'Totally independent. Took me five years to get the script into any kind of shape, then Jerry and I took another six to put the financing together. We've had to recast three times. Can you believe we even had Daisy Ridley lined up at one point about ten years ago, and phht, there went that. Couldn't afford her lunch now. Imagine if we could've made it back then, with where she is now.'

She made a hopeless gesture.

'Will you recover from this?'

'We were already tight,' said Tennyson. 'Zero free space in the schedule. So, even if we're shut down for a day, it'll be tough.'

'You're not just shut down for a day,' said Buchan, and she was nodding as he spoke. 'And it's not just the building, obviously. We're going to need time with everyone involved.'

'You think the film crew are involved?' There was no

resentment in the question. 'It could be an entirely internal church matter.'

'Early days,' said Buchan, and she nodded along with him again. 'Did you know the victim?'

'Yes,' she said. 'That's why I'm not making any assumptions about our innocence. Angus was the liaison between the church and the movie. We'd spoken to the, like the minister and the main guy who set it up, the guy we spoke to in the beginning, he's like the clerk of the kirk session, I think. And there's the guy in the wheelchair with the, you know, the girl that helps him out. Not sure what his job is, but he opens up and closes up. Although, Angus was doing that too. Angus was our point of contact.'

'And who was his point of contact with you?'

'Oscar, the line producer,' she said, then she noted the look on Buchan's face and added, 'You've spoken to Oscar.'

'Oscar never mentioned that he and the victim were on any sort of co-working terms.'

'Look, I'm not throwing Oz under the bus or anything. He's a decent lad.'

'He wants us out by breakfast, so the shoot can continue,' said Buchan.

Tennyson laughed lightly. A nice laugh. She had a defeated air.

'He's sucking up to Jerry. He thinks Jerry's going places, and wants to attach himself to him for the ride, no doubt stabbing him in the back and taking his place the first chance he gets.'

'Is Jerry going places?'

'Jerry ain't going nowhere.' She waved a hand as she said it. 'Who knows? It's that kind of business, right? You pull something off, then suddenly everyone thinks you're the shit, and Brad Pitt and Matt Damon are forming an orderly queue to suck you off.'

She shivered as she said it, then shook her head.

'Sorry. I'm trying not to be tense, you know, whatever, but... you know, I really need to speak to Jerry, we need to start making some calls. God, Jerry's already making calls and I need to know who he's calling.'

'This is your third week at the church?' asked Buchan, eschewing any sense of urgency.

'Yes. We had two days at the start when the building was

12